"From ACORN to ZOO"

AND EVERYTHING IN BETWEEN IN ALPHABETICAL ORDER

SATOSHI KITAMURA

Published by The Trumpet Club
1540 Broadway, New York, New York 10036
Copyright © 1992 by Satoshi Kitamura
All rights reserved. No part of this book may be
reproduced or transmitted in any form or by any means,
electronic or mechanical, including photocopying,
recording or by any information storage and retrieval
system, without the written permission of the Publisher,
except where permitted by law.
ISBN 0-440-83151-2
This edition published by arrangement with
Farrar, Straus and Giroux
Printed in the United States of America
February 1994
1 3 5 7 9 10 8 6 4 2
DAN

From ACORN to ZOO

AND EVERYTHING IN BETWEEN IN ALPHABETICAL ORDER

SATOSHI KITAMURA

A TRUMPET CLUB SPECIAL EDITION

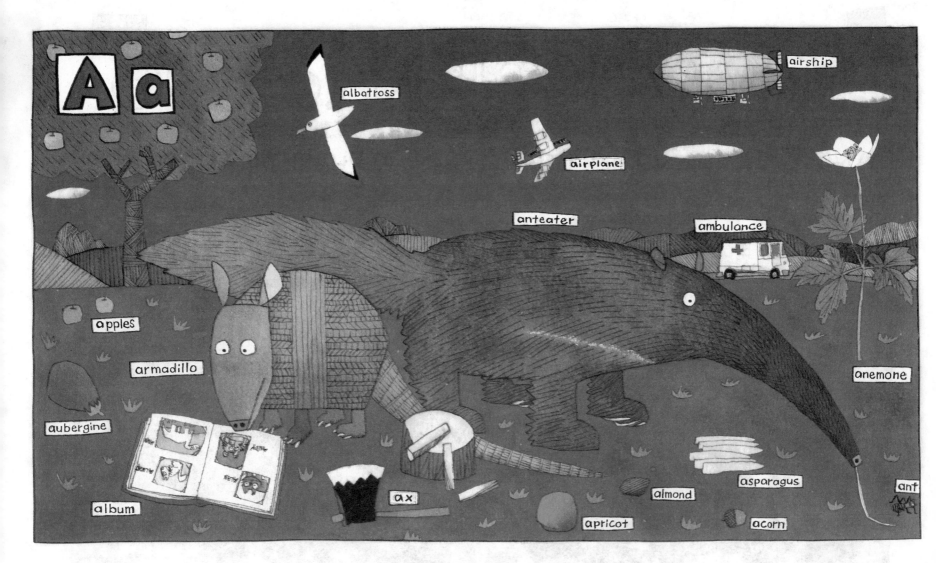

albatross

airship

airplane

anteater

ambulance

apples

armadillo

anemone

aubergine

asparagus

ant

almond

album

ax

apricot

acorn

What is the armadillo balancing on his nose?

Who's watching Baby go up, up and away?

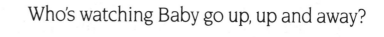

How does a cat toot a tune to charm a cobra?

D d

dove
daffodil
dolphin
dewdrop
dandelion
daisy
dog
duck
drum
dynamite

Why should Dog
and Duck duck?!

Which came first, the eagle or the…?

With what feathered friend does Frog share his fruit?

What is the grinning girl holding in her hands?

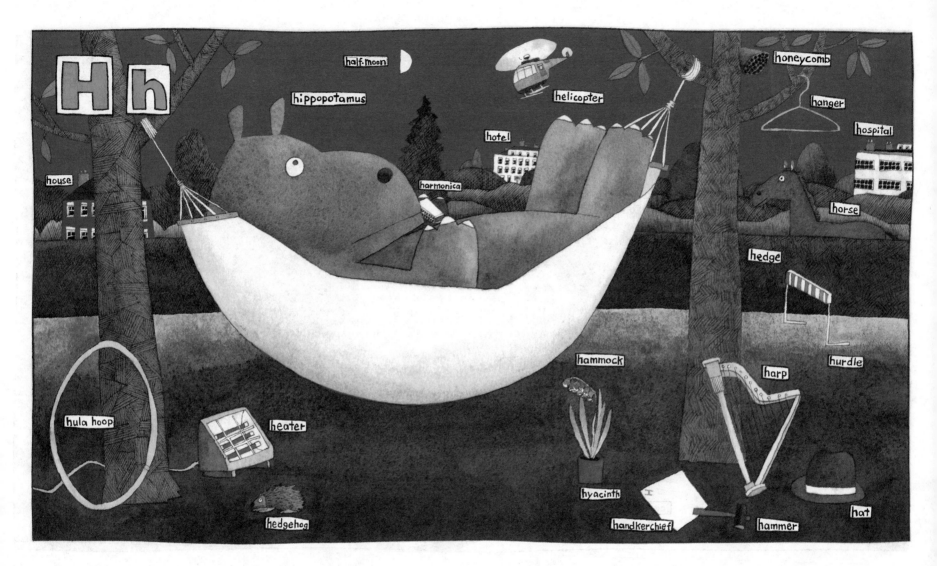

H h

half-moon

honeycomb

hippopotamus

helicopter

hanger

hotel

hospital

house

harmonica

horse

hedge

hammock

hurdle

harp

hula hoop

heater

hyacinth

handkerchief

hammer

hat

hedgehog

Who's hiding in Hippo's hat?

iceberg

ibis

icicle

island

igloo

ice cream

iron

ivory

iris

iguana

ice

insects

ice skates

ink

How does an eager iguana glide on the ice?

What will Jaguar enjoy for dessert?

"Who's sleeping in the kennel?" caws Kiwi.

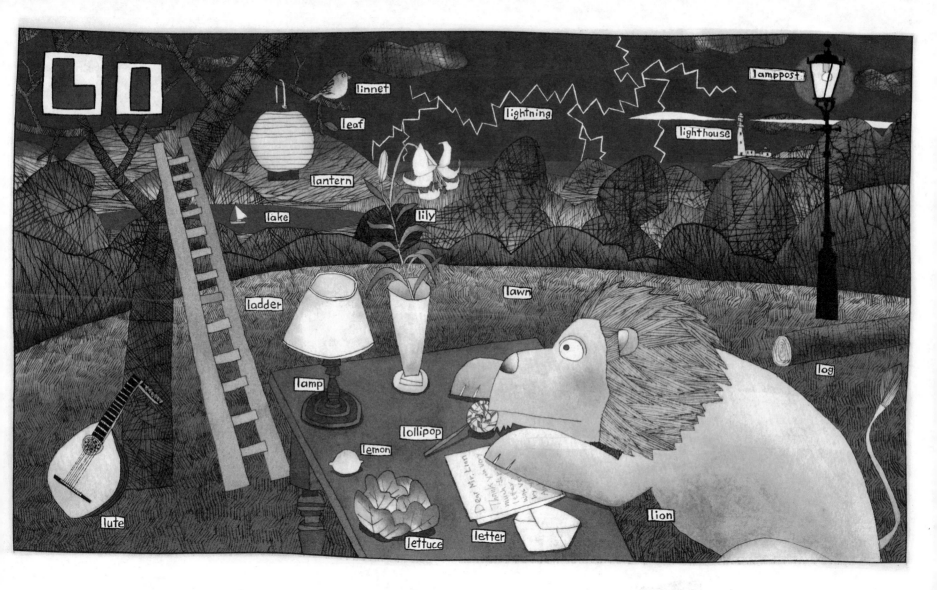

linnet

leaf

lightning

lamppost

lighthouse

lantern

lily

lake

ladder

lawn

log

lamp

lollipop

lemon

lute

lettuce

letter

Dear Mr. Lion
Thank you very much...

lion

How does Lion light up the night?

moth

moon

marigold

mountain

mammoth

mop

magpie

microphone

mushroom

mask

monkey

music stand

magnet

map

matches

microscope

money

mittens

mantelpiece

mouse

mitt

milk

mug

"Boo!" says the masked magpie.
Who does he scare?

What does a natty nightingale wear?

observatory · overcoat · owl · oar · Octopus · ostrich · otter · Onion · okra · Orange · ocarina · oboe

Whooo goes out to
sea with Octopus?

P P

pyramid

pipe

piggy bank

pitcher

pen

pencil

piano

picture book

pine

pelican

potatoes

pheasant

penguin

pineapple

page

parcel

pedals

pillow

What is Penguin putting
in the postbox?

POST

What can a queen use to make her Q's?

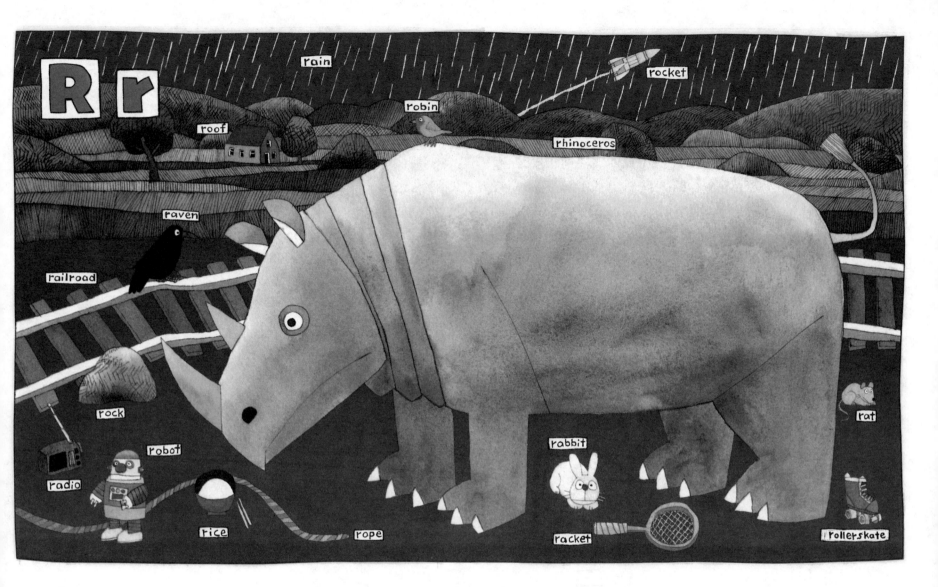

rain

rocket

robin

roof

rhinoceros

raven

railroad

rock

robot

radio

rice

rope

rabbit

racket

rat

rollerskate

How does Rabbit
race along the road?

What should a snazzy sea gull wear
at the seashore?

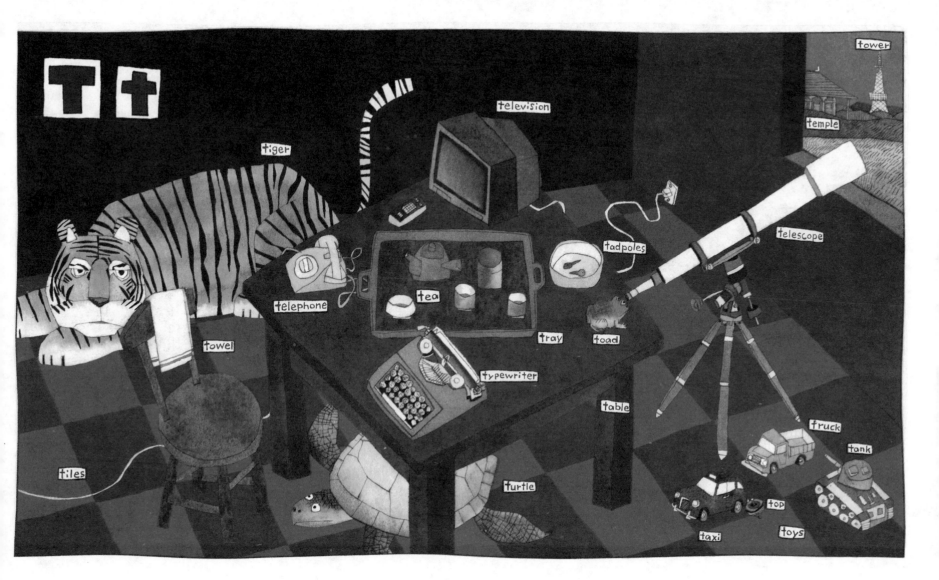

Who watches Turtle while
Turtle watches television?

Up in the sky! What's coming
to visit Unicorn?

volcano

vine

vulture

van

vacuum cleaner

viper

violet

violin

vegetables

vase

Who plays the violin
like a virtuoso?

walls

wings

Wardrobe

warbler

woodpecker

whale

waves

willow

wolf

walrus

wallaby

wheelchair

watch

weasel

window

wool

walnut

wallet

What do Wolf and Wallaby
wear to keep warm?

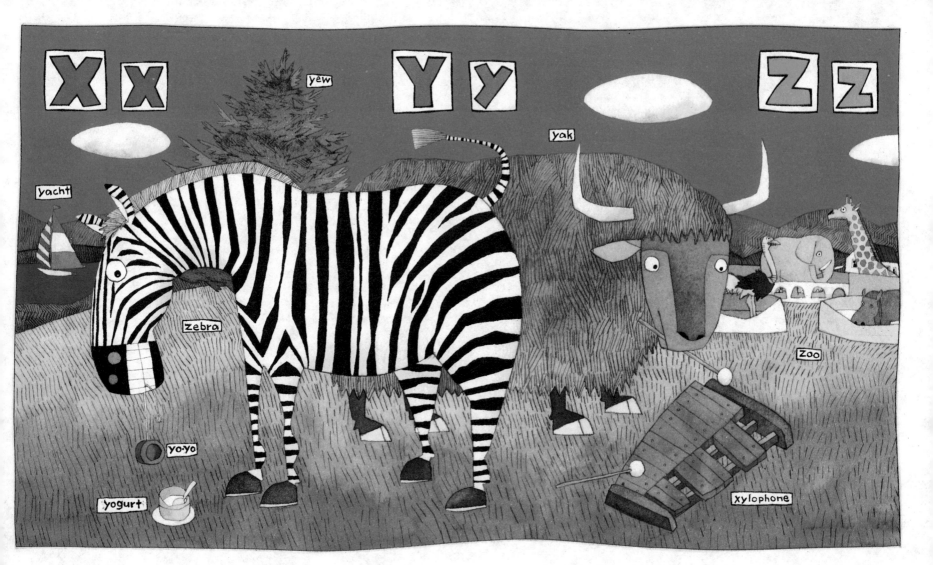

X x yew Y y yak Z z

yacht

zebra

yo·yo

yogurt

zoo

xylophone

Yoohoo! Where are Zebra's friends?